HOORAH FOR THE FILTH-PACKETS!

ALEXANDRA ARTLEY

HOORAH for the Filth-Packets!

Illustrations by Martin Honeysett

Methuen

First published in Great Britain 1987
by Methuen London Ltd
11 New Fetter Lane, London EC4P 4EE

British Library Cataloguing in Publication Data

Artley, Alexandra
Hoorah for the Filth-Packets!
I. Title
828'.91409 PR6051.R65

ISBN 0-413-51630-X

Printed and bound in Great Britain
by Richard Clay Ltd, Bungay, Suffolk

To G.

CONTENTS

I

A Day in the Life of the Filth-Packets

Mr and Mrs Filth-Packet are utterly exhausted. They have spent the night half-consciously strangling each other with ropes of sheet in an unmade bed and hauling the bed-clothes from one side to the other like coal-heavers. As the gregarious Filth-Packets usually retire very drunk, they mountaineer over each other at various times during the night to go and drink half pints of water. During winter months this behaviour disturbs the Pampered Pet which is allowed to sleep in the bed with them. Finally driven off, he makes a cosy nest in a convenient pile of dirty underwear. As the weeks speed by, this knicker nest is comfortably rounded out and achieves a homely lining of moulted animal hair which the kind-hearted Filth-Packets are loath to disturb. As both parties are too idle or preoccupied to buy new wireless batteries, the Filth-Packets start their day with an hour of very faint Radio Three, which comes and goes, as if being relayed from the moon. Mr Filth-Packet irritably leaves the bed when he discovers his elbows and shoulders are rubbed raw with the crumbs of biscuits which he and Mrs Filth-Packet accuse each other of having secretly eaten.

As Mr Filth-Packet runs himself a ringed bath, he thoughtfully peels an appalling elastoplast from his foot, which he folds in half and leaves on the first convenient bathroom ledge. Later in the day, this dreadful object makes a fastidious visitor want to scream and go home without any dinner. Both the Filth-Packets suffer endless foot wounds as one slipper is always lost in the undulating fluff under the bed and the Pampered Pet is allowed to leave sharp old bones in every room in the house. Mrs Filth-Packet only ever wears shoes at home when she is expecting visitors or has spilled granulated sugar in the kitchen. Before they were married, Mr Filth-Packet came to realise he must love her when he could face pulling two-foot clots of soapy matted hair out of slow-draining plug-holes.

Setting about his morning toilet, Mr Filth-Packet abandons the idea of a bath as the water is cold. Shaving is torture as his razor wears a collar of richly congealed lather and the ancient blade is bright orange with rust. Around the tide-marked wash-basin lie four soggy razor-blade packets – all empty. On opening his razor to inspect the blade, Mr Filth-Packet discovers that his wife shaved her arm-pits the previous day. Scattered around are half-a-dozen toothpaste tubes, all capless and all squeezed flat to the very last squeak. Mr Filth-Packet carefully mangles one tube in the hinge of the bathroom door in the hope of getting a further iota. In a chipped commemorative beaker stands his Kent toothbrush, ancient, soft and splayed. Casting round for something to wash with, Mr Filth-Packet gathers together two or three of the watery soap slivers which slowly turn to coloured slime around bath and basin. A whole bar of soap is never seen in the house.

Drying himself with a series of towels all equally damp and stinking, he notices he has cut himself innumerable times while shaving. He completes his toilet by sticking tiny patches of newspaper on his chin and throat to clot the wounds.

As Mrs Filth-Packet only ever gets up in the morning to catch aeroplanes or to let in parcels, Mr Filth-Packet returns to the bathroom to fill the breakfast kettle. This is because the kitchen sink is so full of dirty dishes the kettle will not fit under the tap. On good days the height of the washing-up will permit the kettle to be filled by its spout. As the heavily furred kettle grinds to a boil, Mr Filth-Packet throws up the shutter of a flimsy plastic breadbin and deliberates between the remnants of a cast-iron loaf or a pale blue one. He decides on the pale blue and carefully trims off the outer mouldy crust with a bread saw lashed together with sellotape.

Three minutes after he has lit the grill, Mrs Filth-Packet is warned of approaching breakfast by the flying reek of old kippers and lamb chops whose fats swirl urgently in the grill pan below. Running a knife under the tap for a few moments, Mr Filth-Packet vigorously scrapes some carbonised toast into the sink of soaking dishes, where the pall of black specks lies like soot on a Salford canal. This done, he clears a space on the sticky oilcloth and butters the toast from a packet of rancid half-wrapped Anchor which bears the marks of many previous meals. The marmalade is excellent but sprinkled with curiosities.

Having delivered yet another cup and plate to his wife's bedside, Mr Filth-Packet is relieved to find a shirt he did not know was clean. Throwing it on the tattered ironing board which is permanently erected in the kitchen, he rapidly irons collar, cuffs and a few square inches of front.

Grabbing a complex technical manuscript on which he has dropped jam, Mr Filth-Packet then rushes by bus to the publishing house of which he is a leading editorial hope in troublous times. As his brilliant brain formulates a method by which one publishing idea can be spun off into four separate books, whilst increasing the author's income on all foreign editions, Mr Filth-Packet's typewriter carriage swings left and knocks two sour cups of cold tea into the heavy pall of memos, manuscripts and half-eaten take-aways which lie like compost on his desk.

Back home in bed, Mrs Filth-Packet reads bits of Balzac and dozes fitfully. This 'visualisation' is essential to her creative powers as a promising, but as yet unpublished, novelist. As the midday sun streams in through shredded Regency drapes (ripped by an Oriental Pampered Pet) a huge loop of wallpaper which has hung from the ceiling for the past two years becomes, in Mrs Filth-Packet's mind, an exquisite silken canopy for the seduction scene in her novel. Blowing her nose frequently on coloured tissues which are rolled into innumerable little balls and stuffed by the hundred into and around the appalling bed, Mrs Filth-Packet lights a cigarette and attempts to sketch a scene or two in her notebook.

Huddled masses of suicidal clothes hang from every ledge and door top, although the wardrobes themselves are virtually empty. Whenever an upstairs door in the house is closed, there is a jangling thud as heaps of clothes on dry-cleaners' hangers hit the ground. Acres of shoes stick up like rocks in a sea of grey fluff and the bombed dressing table is a turmoil of old scent bottles, artificial flowers, amusing Catholic Repository kitsch, Mrs Filth-Packet's sturdy Dutch cap and a Dr Scholl's callous file. Years ago the Filth-Packets thought they were on to a good thing with deep-dyed sheets until it was discovered that semen stains show up white. A suspicion of nail parings haunts the dreadful rug.

What a heavenly autumn day. A few minutes before noon, Mrs Filth-Packet decides the sun is over the yard-arm and gets up for a drink. In an elegant wrapper heavy with the scent of humanity she discovers that downstairs the Pampered Pet has had an accident beside the forty-two old milk bottles the Filth-Packets keep at the side of the stove. Recent bottles have a trace of mid-green liquid at the bottom, which is subtly transmuted to a clear and delicate blue in older examples. The oven interior is a morgue of mouldering daubes. As the Pampered Pet circles for breakfast oblivious of his deed, Mrs

Filth-Packet discovers there is not a trace of sherry in the house. As she never gets dressed in the day-time, going straight into *grande toilette* at six, she belts a hand-picked mackintosh which covers her nightdress exactly. Adding a dash of brilliant lipstick, Romany ear-rings and a pair of decaying plimsolls, she nips out to the off-licence. On the way back she buys a pound of braising steak for the Pampered Pet and a copy of the *London Review*.

While the Pampered Pet savages his bloody feast on the hall floor, Mrs Filth-Packet takes her tumbler of sherry to the piano for a few *moments musicaux*. The middle two octaves of notes are white, but the more romantic extremities of the keyboard are lost in grime. On top of the instrument a landslide of torn sheet music, unsleeved *Gotterdämmerung* sets and Electricity Board final notices imperceptibly shifts with the vibration. After toying with a little waltz, Mrs Filth-Packet flops on the shredded sofa to do more visualising. Brutally replete, the Pampered Pet vigorously rips the sofa for a few minutes before hopping up to join his mistress in her creative reverie.

* * *

The sound of Mr Filth-Packet tripping over old wine bottles in the hall tells Mrs Filth-Packet that it's five o'clock. Rinsing two smeary glasses under the bathroom tap, he pours them both stiff whiskys and reminds his wife that nice Herr Bucher of Edelwiess Verlag is coming for cocktails. After the Frankfurt Book Fair he is over on a mopping-up-London trip. Galvanised by the prospect of fun, both Filth-Packets swig their drinks, immediately run a hot bath and heat the iron. Doing a little archaeology in the bedroom, Mrs Filth-Packet rummages through a pile of discarded underwear and after careful inspection with eye and nostril selects the least dirty pair of knickers she can find. She then opens a new packet of Dior tights. In order to save time she applies her make-up before getting into the bath, delving for every cosmetic she requires in a straining handbag full of dried-up chocolate squares, metro tickets, solicitors' letters and finely sifted filth.

Freshly bathed in second-hand warm water, Mr Filth-Packet finds his suit of the evening lying on the floor behind the bedroom door. Back in the kitchen he ignores the swirling bluebottles and, disentangling the iron flex from the Pet's dried-up plate, carefully presses his suit with the skill of a master tailor. On pressing her elegant lace gown Mrs Filth-Packet discovers a huge grease mark from a drunken dinner. Undeterred, she pins a charming arrangement of silk flowers over the splodge and looks divine.

Scented, coiffed and poised for the gaiety, the Filth-Packets are delightful hosts. Drink flows freely and Mr Filth-Packet has a fund of witty yarns which keeps them all in fits. His favourite of the moment is a paper in the *British Medical Journal* entitled 'Penile injuries from vacuum cleaners'.

Here, two eminent sawbones pool their clinical experience of men tragically attracted to the Hoover Dustette. 'The way people live!' tinkles Mrs Filth-Packet merrily.

Herr Bucher is entranced but uneasy. Remembering how his snowy duvets are daily shaken in the Alpine air, he turns his gin and tonic round to find a bit of hairless rim. An insistent stench he thought he did not smell is traced to two dead vases full of retting stems. The low-slung sofa oozes stuffing like a ripe old Brie. In the bathroom Herr Bucher finds The Elastoplast, now buried in a storm of Mycil foot powder.

He begins to panic. Visions of webbed forks and five-day-old soup partially reheated in a scrambled egg pan make him pray he won't be pressed to dinner. He reflects that alcohol, like salt, is one of Nature's disinfectants. Returning to his hosts, his spirits rise at the sight of Mr Filth-Packet hunting for the telephone beneath a wash of Sunday papers. They will be eating out.

Five hours later the Filth-Packets return home very drunk. They love each other very much and downing a nightcap, they tear each other's clothes off and fall into the tousled bed. Later, in the dark, Mrs Filth-Packet decides that she will leave her make-up on – just this once.

II

The Filth-Packets Go On Holiday

Summer mornings in bed are hell on earth. The Filth-Packets stir irritably in their sultry nest, dislodging a plain Digestive and the Pampered Pet which has been scratching all night. If the mad ripping doesn't stop, he will be shaken in a bag with a dose of Keating's. Lost in the sheets, the Radio Three man says the weather may very well do one thing or, indeed, the complete opposite. As the morning concert grinds out Canteloube's dreary old *Songs of the Auvergne*, husband and wife rise as one in a state of panic. They had quite forgotten that any minute they are off to the Dordogne.

Geography flits by in a blur of pleasure. Her mind a sudden whirl of Provençal gaiety, Mrs Filth-Packet seizes a Dr Scholl's callous file and vigorously chamfers her hooves for the strappy look. With grey slough flying as in a stonemason's yard, she muses fondly on the early days in Pimlico when they used to lie in bed ripping a cold roast chicken apart.

Downstairs Mr Filth-Packet is firing on all cylinders. Like all Filth-Packets he is deadline crazy and quite incapable of planning life beyond the next cocktail. In less than five hours he must let the house; finish wallpapering the dining-room in order to do that; book a sea passage; discover the condition of his summer wardrobe; unblock the lavatory; collect Mrs Filth-Packet's replacement passport; pack; implore the vet to make a house call; warn the Company Secretary of an impending lawsuit; off-load the Pampered Pet on to Mrs Filth-Packet's ghastly mother; cancel a stray dinner party; and, most importantly, ring the friend of a friend (who has recently moved to the country and is not in the phone book) to locate their French holiday address. Although it is only 7.15 am, he feels he could do with a drink.

Far below, the kitchen murmurs like an obscure quarter of Cairo. Heavy with the weight of the dead, the ancient fly-papers drift like encrusted mobiles in the balmy air. They are always beautifully illuminated, as Mrs Filth-Packet cleverly leaves the kitchen light on all night to keep the cockroach army in. Pausing barefoot, Mr Filth-Packet is dismayed to find that the muffled retching he thought he heard in the night is confirmed by four salmon-textured patches on the gritty floor. Acutely sensitive to foreign holidays, the Pampered Pet is building up a piteous separation anxiety. His digestion is in tatters and his topaz eyes burn with insecurity as he whines for chunks of breakfast offal. Full of compassion, Mr Filth-Packet spears a boiled lamb's heart from a congealed vat and cuts it small with soothing words. He then wonders, quite scientifically and without acrimony, why animals always throw up in more than one place.

Pouring himself a scalding cup of warehouse sweepings, Mr Filth-Packet traces the telephone cable to its source and frantically begins his talk-athon. He dials Mrs Filth-Packet's mother first, as she is always up at dawn reading Kerouac and searching her compact mirror for *coup de vieux*. The bedside phone is answered instantly, in case it is an agent. 'Monica Hub,' says the thrilling voice of the Fifties' BBC radio actress. Yes, she will collect the Pampered Pet. No, she did not get the part of Penelope Whorehound in the new Dekker. *Nor did she want it.*

As Mr Filth-Packet listens to the seething passions which shape the world of microphone drama, he tucks the telephone receiver under his unshaven chin and dives to the kitchen sink to wash the attached collars of one or two dirty shirts. They will do to begin with, but he hopes there will be a launderette in the Dordogne. Upstairs in the bathroom, quick bursts of plumbing indicate that Mrs Filth-Packet is already washing the feet of thirteen pairs of tights. Although it is a blazing June day, she hangs them on a crippled music stand to dry in front of a one-bar electric fire. As the ancient bar obediently glows red, the wad of fluff on the reflector instantly fills the bedroom with the smell of singeing.

Still on the receiving end, Mr Filth-Packet has no difficulty in keeping his mother-in-law's flow going. She is a woman of formidable vivacity who can run three days and nights on a Scotch egg, ten Rothmans and a bottle of anything. On the Third Programme her acting career was always preceded by the definite article. She always played The Woman, The Boy, The Girl in the Amusement Park or The Voice. Although beautifully articulated from her days in agonising existentialist dramas, that voice is very carrying. She is usually the concert-goer who can be heard saying, 'We always fry ours in lard,' during hushed relays from St John's, Smith Square. She will be round to collect the Pampered Pet in the twinkling of an eye.

* * *

In a bijou apartment off High Street, Ken, which he is only temporarily borrowing, Scott Remington, the first man into Vassar, looks into a warbling Trimphone. The Filth-Packets' number is still engaged. Scott has a Fellow Travelling Scholarship to England to compile *Who's Who In Bloomsbury*, an important reference work with useful charts to show the state of various relationships at given points in time. He is terribly excited as he has just tracked down a butcher's shop which used to sell the Gordon Square scrag end – and what a footnote that will make! The Filth-Packet residence sounds perfect for a discriminating academic visitor like himself.

Again he anxiously scans the ad in *The New York Review* and feels certain the Filth-Packets' line is jammed with eager takers. The English! How he loves them and the whole of that elegant English lifestyle thing. Doing a bit of hoovering to fill in the time, his mind wanders happily over chaste old tallboys, fragrant *pot-pourris* in Lowestoft bowls, glinting fenders and ravishing chintzes. He is as excited as a new bride with a fabric swatch. Adjusting his crisp little Japanese wrap, he winds the hoover flex into a perfect figure-of-eight before trying the Filth-Packet number again.

* * *

As packing requires decision and foresight, the Filth-Packets cannot do it. Instead, they frantically decant the contents of the house from one location to another. Groaning with abuse, their ancient, battered luggage bears the crossed-out stencils of anyone's initials but their own. Built in the days before air travel, it is heavy when empty, impossible when full. A baggage train of plastic carriers supplements the whole. In the brilliant foreign sunshine, curious locals soon try to translate 'J. W. Micklethwaite, Fruiterers of Note'.

Darting through her cupboards like a swallow, Mrs Filth-Packet feels it's all or nothing. In case there is a ball at Perpigny-sur-Mont, she throws in three glamorous chiffons whose floating sleeves have all been wrung out in last year's Vichyssoise. Fearing fickle weather, she adds a foul old oilskin with a fluff-covered sweet in the pocket, two rusty Sabatiers for a stab at cooking and the fearful Filth-

Packet bathing suits, still tight in a mildewed Swiss roll since their last encounter with the sea. Feeling suddenly and unaccountably homesick, Mrs Filth-Packet tops the first case off with a silver-framed photo of the Pampered Pet, some scrofulous tubes of Artists' Colour and a melting box of Harrods' wax ear-plugs to drown the sounds of screeching foreign wildlife.

The phone rings. Even two seconds before a holiday, the Filth-Packets can't resist a party. As he listens to Mrs Filth-Packet's merry, tinkling voice enumerating the purpose and aspect of rooms, Scott Remington thinks it heaven to be a luncheon guest and soon, it seems, a tenant. It is 11.30. As the further beauties of the Filth-Packet residence are unfurled, Scott imagines that to take his call, the gracious Mrs Filth-Packet has just set down her secateurs and stepped in from a fragrant, nodding garden. Perhaps she has been cutting roses for her luncheon table and elsewhere in some airy, Delft-lined kitchen, a pure young fowl will soon be crisping in the finest butter. Miraculously light with pastry, her hands are practical and cool and now come those marvellous English puddings with names like early keyboard music – Mrs Filth-Packet's Whim-Wham, Roxana's Posset or Mr Remington's Delight.

The house has the dubious charm of an old commode. In swift anticipation of company, Mrs Filth-Packet makes a few symbolic passes with the Ewbank, pushes the stiff and evil-smelling floor-cloth round the kitchen with her foot and hurls a lump of mutton at the oven's jaws. Very soon the house is filled with the warm abomination of the tallow factory.

Spotless in his Brooks Brothers' blazer, Scott Remington looks with interest at the blistered door. Behind it lies a cavern filled with dusty wellingtons, old wine bottles, a rusty bicycle, mud-caked garden forks and a cracked mirror which slipped its chain at a Christmas party. Supplicant plants beg passers-by for water. The walls are lined with vibrant Mediterranean landscapes signed by Mrs Filth-Packet herself. Her impasto is so dashing they look like tins of cat's meat thrown at the wall.

The decayed sitting-room is buzzing with alarm. Clinging to his generous gin, Scott blenches as a strapping man in tweeds administers a tranquillizer to the Pampered Pet. It is Jack Roach, a squalid old vet who reeks of whisky, formaldehyde and aged dog. No animal large or small perplexes him as he paints gentian violet on everything. Snarling savagely and foaming profusely at the jowls, the Pampered Pet is having none of it. Kind-hearted Mr

Filth-Packet is almost in tears as he tries to restrain his darling's thrashing limbs.

'That should do the trick,' says Jack Roach cheerfully, as a phenobarbitone is thrust between the barracking jaws. Wiping his burly hand on the terrible tweeds, he then rummages convivially for a cocktail olive. The word 'Rabies' sizzles like poker-work in Scott Remington's brain. Under cover of lively conversation, the Pampered Pet throws the company an old-fashioned look and glides behind the sofa to eject the tablet with contempt. Twenty-six other tablets already lie there. Butter will take the taste away.

The doorbell rings. Moving swiftly on her ballerina flatties, Monica Hub arrives like a blast of Bartok. Everyone is kissed and affectionately screamed at. Knocking back a pretty stiff one, she opens her enormous bag and presents the Filth-Packets with a few preserves of her own making. They are full of crunchy, crystallized wasps. Appalled by the off-stage cooking smells, Scott is gasping for air. Propelling him forcefully by his crisp, seersucker elbow, Monica suggests they take their drinks into the garden. She likes the cut of his jib.

Outside, the transatlantic subscriber to *Garden History* drinks in the view. It is a vista of yoghurt cartons full of failed seedlings, collapsing greenhouses and an ill-favoured fountain which makes a noise like a cart-horse peeing. Twice a year, the premises are raked at by a nice old bore with plugs of greasy cotton-wool in his ears. Through a pigeon-splattered window Scott perceives the Pampered Pet aboard the dining table, hijacking the Anchor.

'Naughty boy!' cries Mrs Filth-Packet, clapping her hands and dispersing the tongue marks with a knife.

The whinnying, shuddering fridge is a cling-wrap Père Lachaise. By its ghoulish light, ruined cheeses, death-defying pâtés and corrupt old gravies lie at rest with Pet's meat portions and strange wee pessaries which need to be kept cool. Divorced eggs are a Filth-Packet speciality. In one corner, thin, greenish whites have been harboured since Christmas for meringues while opposite, in a horrid basin, sluggish yolks are destined for some terrible invalid nog.

Mrs Filth-Packet whips up luncheon in a moment. A fridge is such a boon. As he is steered towards the dining-room, Scott Remington wants to scream. Avoiding the tainted butter, he chokes on a liquefying pâté which could be drunk through a straw. It is accompanied by toast that tastes of grill-pan kippers. Conversing vivaciously, Monica

straightens the silver. Every knife in the house has prised a paint tin. Beneath the window sits a bucket of mouldy paste with a decorator's brush sunk up to the haft. The Filth-Packets started papering the room years ago, but it is still three rolls up and nine to go.

Out in the kitchen the mutton has hit the deck. 'What the eye doesn't see,' says Mrs Filth-Packet gaily, as she blows off some grit and throws it on a nice cold plate. The Filth-Packets eat, swig and talk with gusto. To follow, there is decomposing salad from a thrifty plastic bag, peripatetic cheese and a fruit salad swamp wittily dished in a Doulton chamber-pot. Pleading the heat, Scott Remington passes out.

* * *

Lying weakly on a battered sofa, Scott Remington hears the Filth-Packets finally depart. The small, white Citroen with the broken door is waiting to be off. It is crammed with bags of wet washing to be dried on arrival, groaning luggage, a mangy owl bought in a fit of Victoriana, fish and chip papers, bits of road map, a small chair still waiting to be stripped and half a pair of tights left over from a fan-belt repair. Wedged under the driver's seat, one befouled shoe will scent their journey.

Halfway across the English Channel, Mr Filth-Packet finds a final demand for the phone bill and notes it is ten days old. Collaring the Purser, who loves novelty, he makes his way to the radio room and on a sizzling ship-to-shore line rings North

Central Telephone Accounts, promising a cheque from Calais. He then forgets all about it.

Back home, Monica is looking after Scott. In a hideous, half-washed saucepan some frozen chicken pieces, a torrent of tinned tomatoes and a head of garlic are turning into *poulet Provençal.* Lust rattles in her like a motor mower. Gaining maximum purchase, the Pampered Pet vigorously rips the invalid couch to let Scott know he's starving. Monica takes her glass of robust red to the window. Summer in London can be such fun.

III

The Filth-Packets' Family Christmas

It is Christmas Eve and merry Mr Filth-Packet has four places to dry a shirt. Bawling Christmas carols with innocent relish, he suspends one shirt, of which he has moistened only the cuffs, from a dry-cleaner's hanger at the foot of the stairs. In a stiff draught from the splintering front door, it dongles slightly with Constructivist charm.

Seizing a splayed Addis washing-up brush tufted with scrambled egg, he vigorously scrubs the black collar crease of another shirt. Then he hangs it from the edge of the drawing-room mantelpiece. Two more shirts, of which he has washed only the fragrant junction of underarm seams, hang gloomily like political martyrs from the picture rail in the hall. Having maximised use of the liveliest air currents in the house ('gathering winter FUOO-OO-ELL'), Mr Filth-Packet wonders what to press on with next.

The Filth-Packets love Christmas. Outside the decaying house, two weary bay trees stand done up in droopy pink bows. Humming an ancient catch, Mrs Filth-Packet swoops from house to garden with bales of grimy urban holly. Great is her love of evergreens. Unless something very convivial is about to happen, Mrs Filth-Packet rarely gets dressed. Clanking with Afghan silver, she wears a pair of Mr Filth-Packet's socks, an impasto of lanoline face-pack and an exquisitely embroidered antique kimono with one Madam Butterfly sleeve unfortunately dipped in last week's chicken Madras.

The Filth-Packets are, as ever, deadline crazy and simply cannot plan ahead. Mrs Filth-Packet is in a panic. Although it is nine o'clock on Christmas Eve, she has yet to cut more holly, make and send two hundred witty cards, telephone a stray Swedish diplomat with their address, correct the tilt on the Christmas tree, see if the turkey will fit the oven, re-spray an enormous number of things with gold paint, pack for the traditional Boxing Day dash to her brother's house party at Squeams Hall, stuff fifty Turkish prunes with rather grey home-made marzipan and tan her legs with Teint Doré. Dithering like an aspen, she pours an enormous gin.

Eating a banana, Mr Filth-Packet bounds upstairs. The Christmas decorations must be found. O what a tangled web we weave when first we hang dry-cleaners' hangers on the side of a wardrobe. Rummaging through a forest of twisted wire, Mr Filth-Packet gropes for the three-sided collapsing cardboard box full of gummed-up sprays which harbours the peeling Filth-Packet baubles. It is set in the fluff-filled dip on top of a vast mahogany wardrobe.

The Filth-Packets love dry-cleaners' hangers because their pliant hooks can be bent in any direction to hang on the first ledge that comes to hand. Over the years, Mr Filth-Packet has developed the technique of knowing just how far to bend a hook before it snaps off altogether (most annoying). Tonight fifteen hangers are caught up in a caul of Sketchley's cling-wrap. At last. Mr Filth-Packet is amazed to find that a clump of eight miraculously cling together in his hand like the locked swords held aloft in a Morris Men's triumph.

* * *

An English Christmas! Olaf Perrsön, the lovesick Swedish diplomat, flexed two rather nice sauna'd shoulders in an Aalto chair, his long reindeer face still warm from reading the *Pickwick Papers*. What an age it took to really know the English and their seasonal trad-ition off dan-cing the Rog-er de Cov-er-ley in this Ding-ley Dell. Yaaa, he thought wisely. All north Europeans are for-est peoples at heart, under-stand-ing the phall-ic pow-er of the tree. Like the facades of their beaut-i-ful South Ken-sing-ton terrace houses, the English were so reserved, appar-ently all the same. But if one had the good fortune to pen-et-rate to real family life, what unex-pected warmth and rich-ness of trad-ition one could find.

Throwing back a very modern tumbler-full of aquavit, Olaf sees a drawing-room sparkling with huge looking-glasses and handsome wreaths of evergreen. In a fine black-leaded grate leaps a brightly burning fire with a good deal of mulling and wassailing going on. Angelic voices tinkle from the sweetly shampooed heads of pretty children wearing velvet clothes. They cluster round the Christmas fir, joyously looped Prince-Consort style, and as strong and dark and looming as his Nordic soul.

What are these? Olaf sees elegant presents sashed with scarlet satin ribbons, while outside the window a fine-throated robin boldly sings to a handsome garden breathing quietly under a quilt of snow. Tomorrow Olaf Perrsön would see gracious Mrs Filth-Packet, lover of nineteenth-century Scandina-vian art. Was it really only two months ago they had stood together in the Hay-ward Gall-ery, looking at August Strindberg's very strange picture, *Lonely Poisoned Mushroom, 1893*? Olaf Perrsön is in loff.

* * *

Two miles away, Mrs Filth-Packet gets on with the crib. Even though she says it herself, she *knows* her lovely artistic crib is utterly inspired. 'O Litt-le town of Beh-eh-eth-lee-hem . . .' When it comes to Christmas everything in Mrs Filth-Packet's life has been too pretty to throw away. First she digs out an *exquisite* group of hand-carved Italian Nativity figures, chipped, partially disabled and wearing totally bedraggled clothing. Arranging them in a slightly unconventional way to cover dilapidation, she sticks the Holy Family in front of old match-boxes, cotton reels, small bottles of nail varnish or anything that will prop them up for five minutes on a bed of pet-shop straw.

Next Mrs Filth-Packet inserts a few dusty Expressionist wickerwork oxen, an ass or two and a byre, all made by some halting artistic figure of the Fifties who had briefly lived with her mother. Then twisting its dreadfully bent feet to get a grip, she adds a 90p Chinese dove of peace from Gerrard Street, which hangs on for dear life, symbolising Filth-Packet goodwill towards men.

To produce a cavernous effect, Mrs Filth-Packet zips out in the dark in her dressing-gown and hauls trails of ivy off the back wall, slashing at the turbulent growth with rusty kitchen scissors that are

never seen again. As she does everything at the last minute, there is no time to stick the greenery under the tap before she sprays it with choking drifts of gold paint and artificial snow.

'And the rising of the su-hun and the running of the deah . . .' A bit of illumination is provided by a branch-line of totally unreliable fairy lights led off from the Christmas tree. The casualty-ward electrics are bound up with miles of insulating tape in a twenty-year history of emergency repair. As Christmas is a-truly-lovely-time-and-our-beautiful-crib-means-so-much-to-us, Mrs Filth-Packet strews the straw with delicious fresh flowers, which by Twelfth Night look like a stricken bunch of desiccated grave weeds. 'We Three Kings of Or-ee-ent-are . . .' To finish off the top of the crib, Mrs Filth-Packet pins up an old star brooch bought in a jumble sale ('Georgian paste, SO charming') and which she hopes will catch the light but doesn't quite.

Good heavens! There is only twenty minutes to go before Father Terry Clone's Midnight Mass. Following the yellow liquefying marks of Sellotape Past, Mr Filth-Packet bangs up the dusty crepe in swags. Soon the drawing-room is strung with glory. As a ladder can't be found, he scales and straddles the groaning furniture, manfully leaping from sofa to sofa and from thence to the back of a chair. 'Deck the hall with boughs of HOLL-EE . . .' Rapidly Mr Filth-Packet sellotapes joyous bells and baubles to wads of picture-rail fluff, simulates the romantic swirl of winter by sticking horrible blobs of cotton-wool to the downstairs lavatory window, and with bold confident sweeps, sprays dead summer flies with passing blasts of aerosol silver so they lie upturned on ledges like Egyptian treasure.

* * *

Over the years, Mrs Filth-Packet has discovered that a glass of wine left out on the corner of the mantelpiece all night, tastes much the same in the morning as it did the evening before. It is Christmas Day and thus fortified she starts her cookathon. At all times of the year Filth-Packet hospitality is boundless, but now the lonely hearts pour in. Through a terrible hangover, Mrs Filth-Packet vaguely remembers that an absolutely charming Swedish diplomat ('SO civilised') might be just the ticket for Elspeth Cockbayne ('a sweet and perfectly lovely girl who-would-make-him-an-excellent-wife'). Thank goodness she is so adroit. How would the world go round if happily married women did not make some effort to bring two wandering souls together?

The door-bell rings. It is Olaf Perrsön, whose haunted Nordic eyes sear the peeling knocker like an insomniac searching the sky for hints of dawn. Stumbling through a curious hall full of old milk bottles, a litter tray for going poosies and some half-washed shirts, Olaf enters a strange decaying room, swaying with bits of coloured paper and dominated by a giant stricken fir. It is like a tinkers' clearing in a forest. The Filth-Packets love a proper tree. From floor to ceiling on the lurching fir are strung up shankless baubles looped with fuse wire, good odd ear-rings, pyromaniacal Victorian candles, flaking Twenties' Chinese lanterns, a wizened fairy tied by the waist and tinny bits of Hindu tat. In the tilth behind the pictures some holly darkly puts out roots.

Clapping her hands to dismiss the Pampered Pet from the pastry board ('NAUghty boy'), Mrs Filth-Packet greets Olaf with utter charm. What an extraordinarily good-looking man he is. He melts. On her outstretched hands he is surprised to see that the jewels in her huge antique rings are set anew with some kind of chopped-liver stuffing. Propelled by the elbow, Olaf enters the kitchen. 'You really MUST meet Elspeth.'

Ring out wild bells. In a room swirling with brown reek from the encrusted oven, Elspeth Cockbayne, the Aydenburgh librarian, is amazed to find herself holding a preserving jar tied with a bow. Moody specimens ('DO taste one') hang in it as if in formaldehyde, and on the label a blobby old biro has written, 'Roxana Filth-Packet's Cerises a l'Aigre-doux'. She has never seen cooking like this before. Around Mrs Filth-Packet's Manolo Blahnik feet are stacked many seasonal novelties. Evacuated from the oven's shades lie cabbage caches out on parole, roasting tins set with speckled fat, three jugs of ancient gravy, the wreckage of a crashed duck and mouldering potatoes meant for frying.

God, the fog. Vaguely wiping the oven door with a stinking floorcloth from which falls a shower of old salami strings, a milk-bottle top and a few black things, Mrs Filth-Packet minutely adjusts the gas, because attention to detail is all. Olaf Perrsön looks beyond his love in horror. Strung up like an atrocity between two upturned kitchen chairs, a pair of ancient tights tautly strains a pint of home-made cranberry jelly. Down it drips into a fire-cracked bowl.

Now for the bird. Parting the purple thighs of a monstrous naked fowl, Mrs Filth-Packet converses vivaciously as a heavily bejewelled hand rams home her very own make of delicious apricot stuffing ('the nice thing about cooking for friends is that you know *exactly* what has gone into it'). Will this vulture fit

the oven? Elspeth Cockbayne looks at Olaf Perrsön and sways slightly. It reminds her of a rather unpleasant gynaecological examination she had in the cold spring of '84.

Another bell. It is Sir Raymond Filth-Packet RA, Mr Filth-Packet's widowed and immensely mean portrait-painting father. His enormous group canvas dashed off for the Worshipful Company of Fish Hurlers has created quite a stir. Smoking incessantly ('Am I annoying you, dear Lady?'), he delves into an appalling canvas bag hauling out crumpled packages for one and all. Then he knocks back a pretty stiff one.

Clad in plaid, Elspeth Cockbayne perches brightly on the edge of a shapeless oozing chair. Beneath her, odd springs move strangely here and there with the unpredictability of some men's trousers. Biting into an Elena fresh-cream truffle, which Mrs Filth-Packet accidentally put in the drinks cupboard two weeks ago instead of the fridge, Elspeth discovers an unusual Stilton centre. The choc has a bit of a beard. Groping near the carpet for her glass, Elspeth meets with something long and soft. It is a half-eaten banana, cast down God knows when and lying in a black slashed skin like a hopeless cast-off glove.

Soon the room rings with *cries de joie* as the Great

Unwrapping begins. As everything is far too artistically interesting to throw away, all Filth-Packet presents are endlessly rewrapped in ancient crumpled paper with old scribbled greetings and sellotape scars cleverly turned inside. Sir Raymond Filth-Packet specialises in bogus luxury presents with glamorous foreign wrappers. So witty, such fun. Soon Olaf Perrsön finds himself exclaiming with hoarse joy over a wittily wrapped packet of Rumanian digestive biscuits ('PURE Festival of Britain'); a box of Polish plum chocolates like hand-dipped cockroaches ('extraordinary how you can't get cellophane like that any more'); and thirty desiccated Soviet cigars bought for the bright yellow box and as dry and scentless as old stoat stools.

Somewhere along the line, Mrs Filth-Packet was given a book called *Cooking For Presents* and this she has done ever since. She loves the personal touch. Into odds and ends of dusty old rummers, cracked Regency tea-cups and partly washed stoneware jars from an abandoned cottage hospital she pours and cling-wraps 'Roxana Filth-Packet's Mushroom Ketchup' ('keeps for YEARS, Elspeth'); 'Roxana Filth-Packet's Surprise Prunes' ('the trick is the ginger'); and Roxana Filth-Packet's solid rubber Turkish Delight, which could stand out night and day in the rain and never be any the worse.

Toying with the Pampered Pet for light relief, Olaf's large clean hand stumbles over a startling lump in the fur. Passing on quickly, his hand meets with two rather strange round bald patches, which may or may not be ringworm. Elspeth begins to panic. From a crumpled wrapping paper which says on the reverse, 'Much love, Roxana, darling. Christmas 1981,' she draws out a pair of terrifying second-hand embroidered slippers ('the silk is SO beautiful, Elspeth, I thought they must be Huguenot'). Trembling with horror, Elspeth looks inside. Firmly printed within are ten rather strong brown marks. Quietly she passes out.

'Good heavens!' With theatrical *éclat*, the hopeless fairy-lights plunge the Filth-Packet home into utter darkness. Swinging lifeless Elspeth to the Roquefort sofa in one manly act, Mr Filth-Packet gropes for the first-aid brandy. Olaf has greatness thrust upon him. He is und-er-standing the el-ec-tricity and, holding a candle, he goes.

The cellar door is the entrance to hell. Stepping carefully between piles of rusty paint tins set down the cellar stairs, Olaf goes to bring back light. Rusty nails stick out like demons. Tearing down cobwebs as big as shawls, the Nordic lover soon embraces Edwardian mangles with warped rollers, zinc baths, penitent coal scuttles, gallon plastic containers with a Plimsoll line of sediment, sacks of silver sand for some half-executed building project, wretched deck-chairs too spavined to close, desiccated bulbs never planted and half a ton of nutty slack. Flung across an enamel breadbin, one despairing rubber glove points limp fingers of doom.

BRILLIANT Olaf. As light returns, curtain-up reveals a scene of carnage. Through a hail of apricot stuffing, the Pampered Pet rips his poultry prey into slavered joints while, wasting nothing, Sir Raymond Filth-Packet RA quietly slips away a jar of bogus black-dyed Danish caviar for use in next

year's Christmas hamper. *Quel dommage*, no dinner. Using his publisher's pull, Mr Filth-Packet is on to the Savoy in a flash. Yes . . . no . . . yes . . . table for six . . . yes . . . HOW VERY KIND. They will be dining out and Elspeth Cockbayne faints again – with joy.

* * *

Humphrey Repton landscaped the park. Set in it like a jewel, Squeams Hall shines with frost. It is Boxing Day and up in a white-painted bedroom like a cool garden of chintz lie two enormous suitcases apparently filled with bricks. Moving a two-bar electric fire exactly three feet six inches away from a piece of Jacobean crewel-work, Mr Prout, the butler, travels on castors to fold away in lavender-scented drawers and presses the this and that of genteel life.

He rarely meets with this make of luggage these days. Reverently setting back a croaking lid, he draws out a fragrant kimono with one orange sleeve; six assorted hotel keys all attached to huge clonks; a Gordian knot of filthy ties; an old sock kept for cleaning shoes; something with a sellotaped hem; a Waitrose plastic carrier containing a cable of damp cloth recently wrenched from a washing-machine; a mildewed sponge-bag with pockets full of slime made up of toothpaste, soap and rust from razor blades; a shirt requiring fourteen buttons; a pair of brogues in another plastic bag shaking with clods of earth; a sturdy Dutch cap in a yawning shell, like a plastic oyster; a bottle of whisky, eight ounces of Caribbean sand; a pungent Edwardian dinner jacket; a dreadful bottle of Ambre Solaire; one flip-flop and a snorkle and a rather chic Victor Edelstein swathed silk dress.

Mr Prout is quite unmoved. He has seen it all before.

IV

The Filth-Packets' Country Retreat

It is a Friday evening in spring and in a car apparently sprayed with minestrone, Mr and Mrs Filth-Packet dash to the country in driving sleet. Whizzing past fleeting hedges and whirling barns, they chatter brightly above the sliding *clong* of empty anti-freeze cans, a defunct torch, an Austrian road atlas, that three-legged *chaise longue* ('PERFECT for the cottage') and thudding half bottles of whisky, paraffin and washing-up liquid, all kept rolling between town and country since 1982.

The moment for fine navigation is approaching fast. Soon the Filth-Packets' unspoiled rural home will be in sight. Plunging through a vast handbag glittering with displaced lire from a decade of Italian holidays, Mrs Filth-Packet hunts for the country keys. Through a beige windscreen veiled with fly spatter she keenly notes the cleverly concealed left turn ('so easy once you know it') leading to the unmarked road ('*wonderfully* secluded'), to the axle-testing track with frozen ruts (bump bumpety-bump), to the absolutely charming gamekeeper's cottage of 1840 at the end of it ('REAL rural life').

They have reached The Paragon at last.

Whining with anticipation, the Pampered Pet looks with interest at the litter tray thoughtfully wedged on the floor at the back of the car between an ancient plastic yoghurt-maker and someone's clay-clogged gardening fork. The Filth-Packets unload their weekend cargo in a flash. Diving blithely in and out of the car like a nest-building swallow, Mr Filth-Packet is vaguely surprised to scent a discrepancy between the atmosphere inside and out. As someone spilled a bottle of milk on the back seat five Easters ago, the Filth-Packets travel in a permanent cave of Roquefort. The warm musk of Nature now adds it heady note.

Reaching carefully over the used litter tray ('CLEVer boy') Mr Filth-Packet hauls out villainous bundles of old steel knives, a collapsing cigar box full of artists' pigments, an aluminium saucepan with a revolving handle, stricken rose bushes of aristocratic descent, stacks of terrible old Highland rugs ('VITAL for guests'), an aged trug and a totally rigid hare. Last comes the Filth-Packets' panic suitcase, into which virtually everything in their London bedroom was rammed.

Getting inside The Paragon takes time. As the wire letter basket behind the front door fell to bits years ago, with lightning inventiveness Mrs Filth-

Packet hung an old gaping lizard handbag there in hope of catching the mail. This has never worked. Now, slowly pushing back a three-foot paper drift of soap coupons, mini-cab cards, free offers and parish magazines, the Filth-Packets enter paradise.

Food and fires come first. Swirling with old Russian wool shawls of dazzling peasant workmanship ('SO beautiful'), strings of Balkan amber and a witty artificial silk jacket with underarms rainbow'd from exertion, Mrs Filth-Packet throws a match at the ancient Calor gas stove and whips up steaming Nes in two mugs ringed inside like Saturn. Then she pours an enormous gin.

Throwing open a mouldering cupboard flashing with silver-fish, she carefully selects two Rich Tea biscuits from a resident packet with a mouse-eaten Plimsoll line and rediscovers with joy a totally useless antique eel trap made of fraying basket-work ('a bygone of GREAT interest'). Returning to a creaking hamper of delights, Mrs Filth-Packet gently attends to its weary thongs. Transporting delicate pastry can be torture. Galvanised by the sight of several pools of cold dark gravy within ('why DOES one try?'), her deft and rapid fingers mend the broken pastry lid of her very own pigeon pie.

* * *

Half a mile away in a pot-holed lane two travellers have not stopped simply to admire the view. 'EEE-EEE-EH-EH-UGH. EEE-EEE-EH-EH-UGH.'

What on earth is wrong with the wretched car? Desperate at the wheel of a company Volvo sits Roland Rut, apoplectic editor of the fashionable new glossy, *Rural Living*. Beside him trembles his brilliantly creative food stylist, Rosa Fey, from whose gentle neck clouds of Stephanotis roll like marsh gas.

Every month in *Rural Living* fresh-skinned people with sparkling eyes stood happily in front of the bright blue Agas they had just installed in converted oast houses, windmills, old chapels or kipper-curing sheds ('now an enchanting country home'). In between all this were articles about Starting A Montessori School in Your Village, the moving simplicity of gnarled old shepherds and what to do with Country Manor dried-thyme sachets.

As Roland capers in the darkening sleet trying to trace the fault, Rosa Fey drinks in the sweet-tasting draught of a photographic job well down. Safe in her bag in shot after shot, an evenly browned steak-and-mushroom pie of extraordinary nobility displays its crust on a country window-sill. Beside it in a simple jug shines a dew-drenched bunch of daffodils (cleverly achieved with a sprinkling of tap-water), and a gleaming riding-crop straight from Swaine Adeney & Briggs; while in a silver photograph frame, a soulful girl wearing a tremendous amount of white lace stares with lunatic passion at the hills.

What an uncanny instinct Rosa has for the subtle nuances of real country life! How she loves the lavender-scented drowsiness of country bedrooms on a summer afternoon, merrily crackling logs spurting across polished flagstones from the winter's hearth, or the clear cold trilling of a little brook on a wild spring afternoon!

For a finishing touch she had casually wrapped a bold red-and-white checked cloth around an earthenware dish the pie was baked in to indicate in a flash the rough game-keeperish charm of really robust country food. The creative words she had in mind to accompany this lovely photograph of a pie might be something to the effect that, I wandered lonely as a cloud . . . *but it was lovely to come home to something hot.*

* * *

Higher up the valley night rolls down as Mrs Filth-Packet plans her cottage ornée garden in the dark ('a *wonderful* position and *marvellous* view'). Mentally laying out laburnum walks, a Gothick summer-house and four rose-sprigged arbours, she sticks six Old Blush Chinas in an ancient bucket and never gives them another thought. In the wintry gloom of an elderly lean-to ('my potting shed') sit old plastic putty tubs full of strange weeds grown with homeopathic intent; softening cartons of Cuthbert's slug pellets ('SUCH a pest'); upside-down bunches of ancient heather carted from Scotland; dead sage blasted by frost and a filthy punctured hose.

Slipping into a pair of wooden pattens ('SO useful for going from wet to dry') Mrs Filth-Packet runs with a torch to get fresh eggs. Passing a bicycle cemetery in a hedge, she darts into the oppressive maturity of a long-collapsing hen-house. In it two old bright-eyed boilers peck strands of horse-hair from a derelict Victorian spoon-back chair. Around them are stacked endless bedsteads, tins of gloss paint entirely finished, old teapots for a paraffin party, almost anything made of enamel, Marie Corelli novels and a pile of 78s. Pouncing on two mud-streaked eggs ('CLEVer girls') which may have been laid this morning or last year, Mrs Filth-Packet bears them off for a lovely breakfast treat.

Fires are a man's work. Running through a tremendous number of old sheds, all roofed with corrugated iron, Mr Filth-Packet hunts for fuel. Over the years he has cleverly reinforced this rippling shelter with blue fertiliser bags weighted down with bricks. By the light of a stormy moon, Mr

Filth-Packet throws down some sodden staves on a chopping block sited like a woodlouse Acropolis. Soon his heroic blows ring out to an audience of old sinks kept as useful planters, swags of ancient rubber tubing, piles of broken bricks mossed on all sides, broken-hearted trellis, a rusting oil drum full of grass cuttings, half a bag of builder's sand and an ancient rusty wheelbarrow turned upside down for twenty years.

Coming with a storm lantern to bear him wifely light, Mrs Filth-Packet grandly skirts a widowed Squeezee with no sponge, ladders ancient and modern, the rusty head of a spade but no haft, a mop whose stringy decaying head is full of tea-leaves, and some *bona fide* logs. Feeling utterly exhausted, the Filth-Packets then decide to have a drink.

* * *

Lead kindly light. Lashed by frightful blizzards, the editorial staff of *Rural Living* toil up on foot towards the beckoning glow of the Filth-Packets' cosy home. Through driving sleet they soon make out a rather simple cottage whose terrible cracks are held together by a dozen rusting picturesque iron cramps. Underfoot lies a liquid layer of crunching ash and squidging bread left out for birds. Passing an incinerator heaped with charred tins, silver paper, bleached stalks of corn-on-the-cob and a boot that fire could not touch, the editors of *Rural Living* look with interest at the Filth-Packets' Gothick porch. In its quaint recesses lie old milk bottles, the back-light from a bicycle; mouldering bellows; pungent old wellies with wet grey linings stuffed with horrible wellie-boot socks; the rose from a rusty watering can; a zinc boot-scraper (incredibly bent); blighted hanging baskets lined with black polythene and taken down from rusty hooks; three useless trowels caked with clay; and an ancient J-cloth used for wiping bird spatter from an alfresco lunch table three summers ago and then thrown down to rot. On a decaying wooden window sill eight old gardening gloves are turning soft and black.

Delighted by the prospect of company ('POOR THINGS') the gregarious Filth-Packets fling wide their cottage door and haul the lucky travellers in. Blown in on a blast of hail the rural experts are amazed to find themselves in a low dark cavern swirling with clouds of smoke. It has the spirited confusion of a Cossack horse fair. By the light of Victorian paraffin lamps belching acrid smoke from untrimmed wicks ('a *beautiful* light'), Roland and Rosa note with smarting eyes a surly choking fire of

greenish logs, cupboard doors crazy with Omega swirls of gloop dashed off by Mrs Filth-Packet in a fit of Vanessa-Bell-paints-Charleston, a collapsing *chaise-longue* held up in one corner by three bricks, appalling rag rugs scavenged from country bins for ethnic rarity, a huge diplomatic portrait too funny for London, witty crevices full of seriously cracked Delft and Rockingham, God-fearing texts of decaying needlework ('Love One Another') while over the mantelpiece with baleful eyes two Staffordshire dogs grimily surmount a donging clock.

Alas, no phone. How unbelievable. 'BUT YOU WILL NEVER GET BACK TONIGHT.' Hospitable to the core, the Filth-Packets are galvanised by the prospect of an unexpected dinner party for four. Conversing merrily, Mrs Filth-Packet flings down a Danäe shower of loose-handled steel knives with dark-stained blades and greenish old forks smelling vaguely of metal to provide two more inviting places at her simple rustic board.

Blenching slightly, delicate Rosa notes the authenticity of her cracked and oozing plate. Hunger is the best sauce. As Mrs Filth-Packet slices decisively into a cold and rather cavernous-looking pie ('plucking pigeons is child's play – the feathers just FLOAT OFF') Rosa wonders whether she did not see a hint of feet and beak among the meat. Next comes a curious warm salad of comfrey leaves ('don't worry, Roland, when I boil them the ROUGH HAIRINESS vanishes'); another strange dish of sinister green ('have you ever tried nettles with bacon?'); a boiled horror called Dock Leaf Pudding ('the trick is the oatmeal') and unusually sharp red stuff labelled in a jar, 'Roxana Filth-Packet's Haphazard Hedgerow Jelly'.

Adding a cascade of rich vinaigrette, Mrs Filth-Packet then sets down a plate of utterly terrifying prickly things with leaves that would dismay a mule ('ordinary artichokes are JUST THISTLES you know'). Pleading a headache, Rosa Fey, feeling faint, decides to go to bed.

'This room is EXACTLY as it was.' Holding high a candle in a chipped enamel holder, Rosa Fey sheds authentic light around her drowsy country eyrie beneath the eaves. Before her lies a grim iron bed above whose sagging aura of use hang jingling brass bits held on with sellotape. From the shadows creep a rat's nest of wire leading to a lamp that does not work, a Regency chamber pot with antique stains, a hair tidy on the dressing-table full of someone else's hair, exquisite little nosegays in cracked vases that leak, and a stone hot-water bottle cold as a rock. Just in case she cannot sleep, popular editions of rotting classics (Vasari's *Lives of the Artists*) lie in

chamois leather bindings powdering to red dust. Outside the sleet has ceased. By the light of a hard frosty moon Rosa notes with horror the Pampered Pet crouching urgently over a patch of weeds ('wild sorrel – SUPREME in green salads'). Groaning with misery, she finally passes out.

* * *

Downstairs in the bathroom, fastidious Roland Rut later wrestles with Satan wondering whether to clean his teeth or not. At The Paragon the Filth-Packet bathroom has no wash basin but a green-stained bath whose old brass taps sing gently all day and a loo whose unstable seat moves sideways during important moments. Groping with relief Roland Rut is surprised to find that the loo roll is strangely limp and damp from living on the floor. Dying of steam he discovers that Mrs Filth-Packet nailed down the bathroom window years ago in a fit of security, while alongside the ancient bath sit dissolving slivers of Pears, Wright's Coal Tar with a grimy streak, terrible glasses full of toothbrushes and sediment and decaying medicaments from ancient emergencies and misfortunes.

Staggering to the kitchen, Roland drinks in the room in which he will complete his bedtime toilet.

Standing at a very shallow chipped enamel sink, Mr Filth-Packet merrily cleans his teeth while a forlorn Ascot sputters scalding drops. SP-IT.

Setting aside a little triangular metal drainer full of egg shells, tea leaves and thistle stalks, which will be scrupulously saved for days for the frozen compost heap outside, Mr Filth-Packet generously waves him in. Outside the temperature gently rises, warmer at last. 'What FUN to be snowed in for the weekend!'

It is coming down very fast indeed. Starting to panic, Roland Rut yearns for his stranded car down in the valley, a dozing hulk beneath Nature's kiss. Flinging his splayed Kent toothbrush down on a sloping wooden draining-board joined to the wall with pale blue slime, Mr Filth-Packet depicts with friendly eyes the weekend joys ahead. If she can battle through, they might be joined by Monica Hub ('the ACTRESS Monica Hub'), his mother-in-law and a most entertaining woman who may reach them by midnight or she may not. Quelling Roland's fears ('NONSENSE Roland. There is PLENTY of food'), Mr Filth-Packet itemises more lovely pigeon pies, some of Monica's exceptional jam, a very moving Stilton kept since Christmas and tomorrow, Mrs Filth-Packet will probably bake her very own bread. Tipping the goodnight dregs of four pale green milk bottles into a ghastly yoghurt-maker ('an ancient Balkan food'), Mr Filth-Packet happily foresees the pioneering help of a capable expert in country matters. Tomorrow in a blizzard Roland Rut will move the hen-house. Rural living has just begun.

Onward and Upward

Happily oblivious to decay and death, the gregarious Filth-Packets move swiftly from one social peak to the next. Soon there will be the June wedding of a long-lost cousin's daughter ('you are an ANGEL to take the catering in hand, Roxana'); the blitzed Tuscany villa reached with a car-load of fainting friends, fellow-travelling Gorgonzola and more wet washing; the mildewed garden party ('DO look into the summer-house, Hortense') for the visual gazelles of *Intérieurs d'Aujourd'hui*.

Inwardly, despite the convivial turmoil, the Filth-Packets are a marshalling yard of disparate detailed information. They strive to make a luminous internal order no matter what their outward life suggests. Unlike those who fiercely clean to expiate their inner horrors, the Filth-Packets have that fine serene ability to sift and organise the nebulous concerns of life. For them, and for all Filth-Packet brothers and sisters everywhere (are you?), the most important chaos has been conquered.